Backpacks
and Bumblebees

John McInnes
Emily Hearn
Lorill Hanney

Nelson

Contents

Backpacks

What's in a backpack?
camper's cargo:
matches   knife   dungarees
flashlight   maps   herbal teas
What's in yours?

What's on the trail ahead?
nature's newscast:
wild flowers blossoming
tree roots twisting
chipmunk scampering
lone deer watching
Ssh!   Stop!
Who's got a camera?

Time at last to set up camp:
unpack backpacks
pitch the tent
chop some wood
tape up nasty blisters
light a fire—
smell that food
Anyone for flapjacks?

Christine McClymont

Weird

Wynne Millar

The three of us zoomed along on our ten-speed
bicycles. The twins, Wilma and David, couldn't
keep up with me, and I wasn't waiting for them. I
had that Saturday morning feeling, as if I could go
flying along with the clouds.

We were heading down to the lake to our favourite place to play. Our parents were still setting up the tents at the camp grounds. There was lots of work to do but they let us go anyway. They're pretty good sometimes.

As I pedalled along I passed an apple orchard. Some men were cutting down trees with a chain saw. I pedalled faster to get away from the terrible noise. But I could still hear it when I stopped my bike on the beach.

I ran to the old willow tree. It leans out over the lake, and it's easy to climb. From up there you can see the little waves push themselves into bigger and bigger waves. I was watching the waves when David came skidding across the sand and hopped off his bike.

"Come on up, David!" I shouted. "The broken branches make good foot-holds. Try them!"

David made his way up the tree, climbing branch by branch.

Wilma was last to arrive as usual. She leaned her bike carefully against the sand bank. Then she knelt down and poked around the roots of the old willow tree. I called to her to come up, but she shook her head.

"It doesn't look safe to me, Marianne."

The waves had washed away most of the bank and left the roots hanging in the air.

David and I climbed down. Wilma was picking up beach stones and clam shells near the roots. Wilma is like that. She stops and looks at everything.

I crawled under the roots. "It's a natural fort," I said to David. "The waves have done most of the work for us."

David poked his head in behind me. "Yeah, all we have to do is tunnel a little farther into the bank", he said. "Let's get our equipment."

That didn't take long. The shovel and hatchet were strapped to my bicycle carrier with my pack. While we were gone, Wilma hadn't moved. She was sitting cross-legged on the beach. She held up a smooth white stone she was polishing.

"How do you like my 'worry stone'?" she said. David wanted to know what it was for.

"You rub it when you're afraid," Wilma told him.

I shrugged. "Who needs a worry stone? Let's start digging."

I guess I'm the leader because I usually think up the things to do. So I said, "We'll take turns digging out the sand. Then we'll spread it around the beach so no one will know we have a secret fort here, okay?"

David nodded. "Okay, Marianne. We'll use the camping hatchet to cut back some of the roots. That will make it easier to get in and out."

I crawled in to dig. There wasn't much room to work, but every shovelful of sand I got out made it better.

David had trimmed away all the roots spreading over the sand. He was chopping at the big thick ones.

"It looks like a monster mouth—with ugly fangs," said Wilma. She imagines a lot of things.

David and I traded the hatchet and the shovel and Wilma went back to spreading sand. Every now and then she would stoop down and pick up a clam shell. She already had a little pile of them.

By the time we stopped to eat lunch the fort was almost finished.

David bit into a cheese sandwich. "I hope no one wrecks it after all that hard work."

"Don't worry. I've taken care of that," Wilma said. "There's a magic horseshoe around the entrance. It's made of clam shells. No one else can cross over it."

David and I looked at each other. Then we looked at Wilma.

"A magic horseshoe? Where? I don't see it."

"No one can," said Wilma. "It's buried under the sand. But we're the only ones who can cross over it because it's magic."

"Where'd you get that idea?" I asked.

I read about it."

David swallowed a mouthful of pop.

"Sometimes you're weird, Wilma."

"Yeah. Really weird," I agreed.

While we were eating lunch the wind pushed big purple clouds across the sun, and the spray from the big waves drifted over to us. I stuffed my left-over lunch and empty pop can back into my pack and said, "Let's hurry and finish the fort. We can keep dry inside if it rains."

We went back to work. Just as I threw out the last shovelful of sand I heard something strange. It wasn't thunder. It sounded as if the old willow tree were moaning.

Then the big ugly monster mouth began to close over me.

"Help!" I yelled.

There was a loud CRUNCH. The monster fangs bit the sand as the willow toppled into the lake. It rocked on its big branches. If it hadn't I would have been squashed as flat as Wilma's worry stone.

A big wave rolled up the beach. When I tried to scramble under the roots, the wave hit me in the face. I was sputtering and gasping. Then my legs folded under me. Sand slid down and covered them. I was trapped.

David picked up the hatchet and began to chop at the roots. Wilma began to claw at the sand. They worked hard, but more sand kept sliding in around me.

"It's no use, Marianne," he said.

The twins stared at me as though they were waiting for me to tell them what to do. I didn't feel like the leader anymore. I was scared. Then I heard the chain saw.

"The men cutting down the apple trees! Go get them!" I said.

David ran toward his bike. Wilma took the worry stone from her pocket and put it into my hand. "Rub on this, Marianne."

I shivered as I watched the clouds push each other around the sky. My Saturday morning feeling was gone.

It began to rain, and the wind pushed the waves higher up the beach. Now and then a big one splashed in my face. What if they got bigger? They'd roll into the monster mouth and drown me. I rubbed the worry stone between my fingers.

Wilma traced out her hidden clam shells with the heel of her shoe. She lay down and curved herself around the magic horseshoe. The waves rolled up and broke against her back. She was keeping the waves away from me!

David seemed to be gone a long time, although I'm sure it wasn't more than half an hour. I felt cramped. "I'll never be able to ride my ten-speed again," I said to Wilma. "I can't feel my legs!"

Before she could say anything, we heard noises somewhere down the beach. Wilma forgot about keeping the waves from drowning me. She jumped up.

"David's back!" she cried.

I heard shouts and then David was grinning at me between the roots. "They're here to get you out!" he said.

David moved away and I saw a man bending over a big chain saw.

"This saw will make a lot of noise," he said. "But the noise won't hurt you." He pulled the cord. The saw screeched. I wanted to watch him cut off the roots, but the sawdust made me shut my eyes.

At last the saw was switched off and the men lifted me out. When they set me on my feet my legs wobbled so much I had to sit down. Wilma and David were crying and hugging me. But I was looking at my legs.

"My legs feel good now. I can ride my bike!" I said, and began to laugh.

"Not today. We're loading your bikes into the truck and taking you back to the camp grounds with them," said the man with the saw.

On the way home in the truck, Wilma held up a piece of the old willow root.

"I'm going to put it under my pillow. Maybe the Fang Fairy will leave me a quarter."

"Wilma, you're . . ." David began.

"Weird?" I broke in. "Oh no, she's not! Remember, her magic horseshoe saved me from the waves. And her worry stone kept me from being too scared."

"I wasn't going to say 'weird'," David said with a laugh. "I was going to say, 'Wilma, you're terrific. I couldn't ask for a better twin!'"

16

It's Raining

Hear the sound of spanging rain
Flicking on the window-pane,

Playing ping-pong with the shutters,
Turning somersaults in gutters,

Bouncing off bike handlebars,
Toe-tapping on the roofs of cars,

Swish-swish, soft as paint-brush,
WHOOSH! tremendous gurgling gush!

Splatter, clatter, reckless rain
Flinging headlong down the drain

Slows to steadier, quiet beat,
A windshield wiper's "wet-feet,
        wet-feet, wet-feet . . ."

Emily Hearn

The Visitor

Karleen Bradford

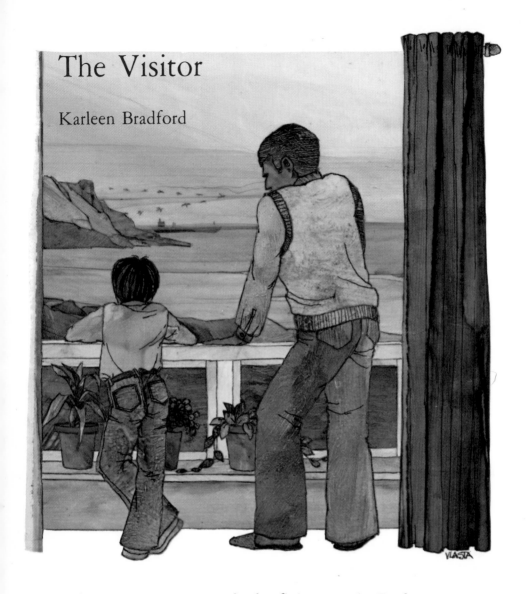

"There go some more ducks flying south, Dad.
Winter's coming for sure." Robbie stood at the big
picture window in his living room, looking out

across Georgian Bay. A "V" of ducks was flying low across the water, and the lights of an oil tanker could just be seen in the dusk. It was early November. Snow had not yet come to this part of Ontario, but it was very cold and raining heavily.

"Br-r-r! I'm glad I'm not out there." Robbie shivered as he climbed the stairs and got ready for bed.

During the night the temperature dropped even more, and when Robbie went out early the next morning everything was covered with glistening ice. Even their own little cove had frozen over. As he walked towards it to take a look, he cupped his mouth in his hands and breathed hard to warm up his fingers. His breath came out in frosty puffs, and he hopped a few steps to keep his toes from freezing. As he drew near a marshy spot by the shore he saw something dark among the reeds.

"That's funny," he said out loud, "That looks like a duck!"

He walked up to it curiously, expecting with each step he took that it would fly away. It lay perfectly still, however, and when he reached it he could see why. Its body and head were covered in greasy black oil and it was frozen fast in the ice.

At first Robbie thought it was dead, but when he
touched it, it made a weak attempt to fly. Gently
Robbie slid his hands underneath and started
freeing the feathers, one by one. The duck
struggled as Robbie worked, but it was growing
weaker. When he finally had the feathers loose, he
took the duck carefully in both hands and ran
back to the house.

"Mom, look what I've found!" he cried as he kicked the back door with his foot. Robbie's mother opened the door and he rushed straight through to the kitchen. "It's a mallard, Mom, and he's nearly dead. I found him frozen in the ice."

"What in the world has he got all over him? It looks like oil," his mother said.

"It's oil, all right," Robbie said. "That tanker we saw last night must have dumped some."

"What are you going to do with it?" His mother grabbed a cloth and started mopping at the dripping oil and water on the floor.

"I'll have to clean him off somehow, if he's going to live, but that's an awfully hard job. Remember that program we saw on television last week? It was about those people who were using detergents to remove oil from seabirds off the coast of England. They said that a weak mixture of detergent and warm water worked best."

"It's after you get them cleaned up that you have to watch out, though," said his mother. "If they don't get their natural oil back they still won't live. Their feathers won't be waterproof. They'll either get waterlogged and drown, or freeze to death."

Robbie held the duck while his mother mixed some dishwashing liquid and warm water in a large bucket. Then, holding the duck as firmly and as carefully as he could, Robbie lowered him into the water. The duck struggled with a new burst of energy, but Robbie held on. He worked away at the feathers with his fingers, washing them off and smoothing them down. When at last he thought he had got off as much of the oil as he could, he lifted the duck out and wrapped him in a big old towel that his mother had brought him.

"Take him and put him down in that pen that we made for the neighbour's dog when we kept him last summer," said his mother. "It's good and big and has a little house at one end that I can fill with straw for him."

In a short time the duck was nestled into the bed of straw and lying quietly. "I guess that's all we can do for now," Robbie said, but he continued to crouch down and peer in at the duck through the wire.

The next morning Robbie was up and out at the duck pen before his mother and father were awake. He knelt down to look. The duck was lying as he had left him. The dish of water beside him was still full and the corn he had scattered around was untouched. Robbie walked slowly back to the house.

At school that day he found it hard to keep his mind on his work, and when the three-thirty bell rang he was the first one out. He ran all the way home and arrived at the duck pen out of breath. The duck was up and pecking at the corn. As Robbie watched, the duck drank a bit of water, then settled down to groom his feathers. First he poked sharply with his bill at the oil beneath the feathers on his beak. Then he drew his bill up around his tail to get it well coated with oil. The duck was coating his feathers with his own natural, waterproofing oil! Robbie watched with delight for a few moments and then ran for the house.

"He's going to be all right, Mom! He's really going to be all right!"

Robbie's mother came running out, and together they watched the duck working away at his feathers.

Two weeks later it was a very different duck that strutted up and down the pen, quacking for his corn whenever Robbie was late. He had put on

weight. The brown and grey body shone sleekly, and the proud green head gleamed in the wintry sunlight. The white around his neck and the bright blue patches on his wings stood out brightly and clearly.

"Doesn't he look great, Dad?" Robbie said as he showed him off to his father one afternoon. "He comes running to me as soon as he sees me in the morning, and he almost eats out of my hand. Pretty soon he'll be so tame he'll probably follow me around like a real pet!"

"Robbie," his father answered seriously, "you're going to have to let him go very soon."

Robbie looked away quickly. "I know," he answered, with a sudden hollow feeling in his chest. "I've been thinking about that." He turned away from the pen and scuffed at the gravel under his feet.

The sun went behind a cloud at that moment, and Robbie pulled his collar around his ears. The wind suddenly had a colder bite to it and the smell of snow was in the air.

"If we wait any longer it will be too late for him to fly south," Robbie's father continued quietly, "and we've got to let him loose before he forgets completely how to take care of himself."

"I know," Robbie answered again slowly, "but how can we be sure that he'll survive? We don't even know that his feathers are completely waterproofed again."

"We'll move the pen down to the shore so that most of it is in the water. If we each lift one side we can walk it down slowly with the duck still inside it. Then we'll see how he does in the water."

The next day they came out to check again on the duck. He was swimming happily around in the small square of water. As they watched, another "V" of ducks flew by, calling to each other. The duck in the pen seemed to hear and understand. He grew more and more excited, swimming back and forth and answering the passing ducks. As they disappeared out over the bay he flew against the wire mesh, beating his wings in his efforts to get out.

"We're going to have to let him go, Rob," his father said.

Robbie reached for the latch of the pen, hesitated for a moment, then flung it open. In a flurry of feathers the duck was out and flying—a bit shakily at first, but soon his wings beats were strong and steady. He flew straight down the bay, heading south, and then he was gone.

Robbie stood watching after him for a long
time. When he became aware of the first fine snow
driving against his face, he hunched his shoulders
and turned away. His duck was free once more.
Free to live or free to die—he didn't know. But he
had done his best.

If I Could Shrink

If I could shrink and still be me
I'd shinny up a daisy tree
And look out over blades of grass
To watch the jungle creatures pass.

I'd be among a million ants
And bumblebees in spotted pants,
Bugs plain and bugs with stripes
Fat bugs and bugs like pipes.

If jet mosquitoes zoomed overhead
I'd scramble down to the flowerbed—
Hitch a caterpillar ride
And dive for a swim at the dewdrop-side.

Emily Hearn

29

Close-up on Bees

Mary Robson

Meet the Bee

Have you ever looked a bee right in the face?
Well, here she is, complete with a pair of large eyes
and two feelers, or antennae, on her forehead.

The bee's antennae act as both ears and nose.
She can smell with them very well, hear with them
a bit, and feel things with them too.

Her big eyes are made of thousands of little
lenses. The bee can see quite well in almost every
direction.

A bee uses her tongue like a straw to drink
nectar from flowers. If you want to know what
nectar tastes like, pick one of the tiny flowers from
a head of clover and nibble the lower end of it.
That sweet taste is nectar. The bee turns nectar
into honey inside her body.

Bees eat pollen as well as honey. They carry it
home in "baskets" on their back legs.

Look in the Hive

Bees live in large families, or hives. Each member of the hive has its own part to play.

The mother of the hive is the queen bee. She is much bigger than the other bees and her only job is to lay eggs. In one summer she may lay about 200 000 eggs.

The queen bee has helpers, called worker bees. They are females too, but they don't lay eggs. They gather nectar and pollen. A single worker bee may visit 250 000 flowers a day. Some of the workers stay home. They make wax from their bodies to build the honeycomb. They guard the hive and keep it cool by fanning their wings. And there's always a clean-up squad to keep the hive tidy. The workers also take care of the queen and the young bees. As the queen moves about the hive laying eggs, the workers fan her and clean her. In a few days each egg will hatch into a small white grub with a big appetite. The workers will have to feed it 1500 times a day! In about ten days the grub will have changed into a full-grown bee, ready to join the other 80 000 bees in the hive.

The male bees are called drones. The drones don't do any work at all. They don't even feed themselves. The workers have to feed them as if they were babies!

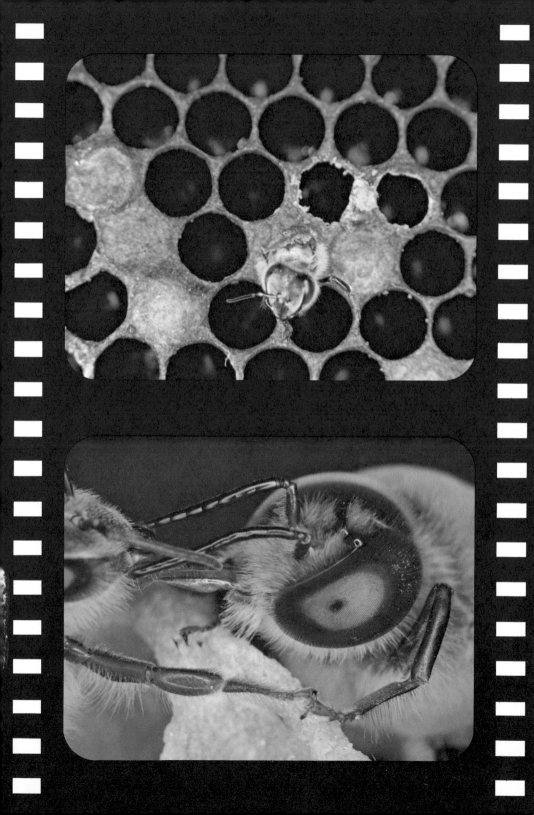

And Then There's the Bumblebee

Bumblebees are larger and fuzzier than honeybees. They don't work nearly as hard as honeybees because they don't store honey for the winter. Bumblebee nests are smaller than honeybee nests, usually containing only 50 to 100 bees.

There is a little beetle that likes to live in bumblebee nests, eating bits of pollen that the bees have dropped. It does not seem to do the bees any harm. In fact, it does some good by cleaning up the nest. The beetle gets to the nest by hitching a ride on a bumblebee's leg!

Watch That Stinger!

Many birds and small animals will attack bees. Bears, badgers and skunks will raid bees' nests for honey. But the bee can protect herself with a stinger she carries at the end of her body. A bee won't usually attack people. When she flies around you, she's probably just being curious. So keep calm and don't try to chase her away by waving your arms. You may only frighten the bee into stinging you!

Tina's Breakaway

Dennis Pelrine

"Come on, Tina," George said to his sister, "you ask them."

"I don't want to," Tina told him. "How about you asking?"

"I guess I don't want to either. I sure wish we could play, though.

"So do I. Kids were friendlier back home in our town. I wish we were still there," Tina said. She scraped her hockey stick along the sidewalk as they watched the boys and girls playing ball hockey on the quiet, dead-end street.

George and Tina stopped talking as they watched one of the boys get a breakaway. With two boys and a girl chasing him, he ran toward the net, braced, then fired a shot high over the net.

"We could have done better than that," Tina said. Then they watched the ball bounce off the curb across the street and come back toward them.

"It's going to go down the storm drain," George
said as he jumped up and ran.

He didn't think he could get there in time, but
he gave it a good try. At the last moment, he stuck
out his stick, but the ball took a bounce, went
over his stick and down the drain. Just then three
of the players reached him, all out of breath. A
boy with freckles stood angrily in front of George.

"Hey, What do you think you're doing?" said the boy. "You just lost our ball!"

"Sorry," George told him. "I tried to stop it but I guess I missed."

"You didn't miss," a girl told George. "You *let* it go down the drain."

"Well," said the boy, "I guess that's the end of the game. Nobody has another ball."

"We have a ball," Tina said. She tossed a green tennis ball into the air and caught it. "Will you let us play?"

"Well . . . okay," the boy said, seeing Tina's smile and George's hopeful look. "We didn't know you wanted to."

"You're new around here, aren't you?" a girl asked.

"Yes, we just moved in yesterday at number 26. My name is George and that's my sister Tina."

"Hi George, hi Tina. My name is Steve," said the boy. "This is Jon and that's Kim and that's Bani, the guy with the red shirt."

"Come on, you guys, let's get the game going," called one of the boys from up the street.

"Okay," Steve said. "George, you'll be with the Leafs and your sister can be with the Canucks."

"Who owns the skateboard?" Tina asked.

"Ivan," someone told her. "Why? Do you want to ride it or play hockey?"

"I don't want to ride it," said Tina. I just thought that if we put it in front of the storm drain, we wouldn't lose another ball."

"Hey, that makes sense," said Steve. He ran to get Ivan's skateboard and placed it in front of the drain. "Why didn't we think of that?"

"Okay," Bani told the newcomers, "it's eight to seven for the Canucks. Ten goals is game. Let's get going."

As the game started again, the Canucks took the ball behind their net and started out. Tina was pleased when one of the boys passed the ball to her. She carried it about half way toward the Leafs' net. She saw two boys closing in on her, so she made a pass.

Steve took the pass and shot in one movement. The ball went into the top corner of the net. There were some cheers and some groans as well.

"Hey, that was a nice pass, Tina," Steve told her as they moved back toward their goal.

"That was a nice shot, Steve," Tina said. Then they stopped talking as the action came toward them.

George was carrying the ball on his stick. As Steve made a stab at him with his stick, George pulled the ball back and started around him, but Tina was ready for the move.

Their sticks met with a crash and the ball went straight up. George slapped the ball down and it went straight to Kim. As she got her stick on it, she turned and took her shot.

Jon, who was playing goal for the Canucks, saw the shot coming and was sure he could stop it. He stuck out his right hand and waited for the ball to hit. It didn't. Instead, it went under his hand and into the net.

The action went from end to end with lots of shouting. When one shot missed the net and went straight for the storm drain, everybody yelled. Then they saw it hit the skateboard and bounce back.

Tina felt proud of herself. She knew the others would remember it was her idea to put the skateboard there.

The score was nine to eight for the Canucks. One more goal for the Canucks and it would be over. George picked up the ball, ran towards the Canucks' net, and shot it between the player's legs. Before the goaltender could see what was happening, it was in the net. The score was tied, nine to nine.

"All right," a man called from a doorway, "it's time for dinner."

"Aw Dad," Kim called, "the score is tied. Just one more goal, okay?"

The man looked at his watch and shrugged. Kim knew he would let her stay for the final goal.

"Well," the man said as he came down the walk, "I might as well watch the action."

Now every player was extra careful not to make mistakes. The two goalies were at their best and it began to look as if the game would go on forever.

As the game continued, other doors opened and parents watched. A lot of dinners were ready, but none of the parents wanted to spoil the game.

They all came down to the sidewalk to watch.
That made it more exciting for the players.

Bani got a breakaway for the Leafs and everyone
was yelling. Running at him from behind, Tina
pushed her stick out and stole the ball from him.

As she turned to go the other way, the rest of
the Leafs came her way. It looked like a whole
wall of players, but it didn't scare her. Instead of
going straight ahead, she stopped. As they moved
to check her, she ducked through.

Suddenly, she was alone. She had a breakaway!
As she stick-handled the ball she saw the Leaf
goaltender in the net ahead. He stood in the
middle of the net, waiting to see which way she
would come.

Tina had seen enough games on television to
know that her best bet was to keep him
wondering. She ran straight at him, watching
carefully to see whether he would move to the
right or the left. But he was a very cool goalie and
he held his ground.

Then there was no more time to think of how she would shoot. She was almost at the goal. The goalie crouched, staring right at her. Then as she came still closer, he stuck his stick out to knock the ball away from her.

That was what Tina had been waiting for. Instead of taking a hard shot, she just pushed the ball gently. It hit the goalie on the inside of his left foot and bounced into the net.

There were loud cheers and groans—some of them from the parents.

When George and Tina went home for dinner, they were tired but happy. They couldn't wait to tell their father about the game.

"Tina scored the winning goal," George told his father. He was proud of his sister.

"So you made friends?" their father asked.

"Oh sure," Tina told him. "I guess kids here are the same as everywhere else."

"I think you're right. And I hope the grownups are as nice as our friends back home. After all, I begin my new job on Monday."

"Well, we had some lucky breaks today. Maybe you will too," said Tina.

"You have another lucky break coming," said their father. "We're going out for pizza!"

Sports to Dream About

Do you dream about being in sports—maybe even being a sports star? Which sport do you dream about?

Skiing! It's the fastest winter fun you can have. Imagine yourself speeding down a steep hill. You'll need skill and courage to stay on your feet!

Speed-skating! If you practice,
you can skate much faster than you can run—
and you don't need any hills.

47

Maybe you dream about
being a gymnast. Can you
see yourself doing cartwheels
and flips across the floor?
It may look easy, but it takes
practice to look that smooth.

High-jumping! That cross bar is almost two metres off the ground, and you feel as if you're flying over it!

49

Do you dream about tennis? Speed and timing are
most important. You have to keep your eyes
on that ball, and be ready when it comes over the net.

How about swimming?
Imagine yourself at the edge
of a pool. The race is
about to begin. You dive in.
Suddenly you're out in front,
heading for an Olympic medal!

Do you dream about being
in sports? Maybe you can
make your dream come true!

51

OLYMPIC TORCH

fire
tumbles
                    pole-vaults
jumps
        dives
                    wheels
races
    slaloms
            spins
                        turns

        figure- eights—

            fire—
            athlete
            superb

    MAGNIFIQUE!

        no wonder
            it
        sets off
            the
        OLYMPICS!

    Emily Hearn

When the Game is Over

Michael Barnes

Debbie was made a reporter for her school newspaper. Her first job was a hard one. She had to interview a famous sports personality. Debbie was fortunate. A man who used to play Canadian football lived in her town. She decided to interview Doug Collins.

DEBBIE: Mr. Collins, how long were you a professional football player?

DOUG: I played left tackle for seven years with the Ottawa Rough Riders and one year with the Hamilton Tiger Cats.

DEBBIE: Many boys and girls would like a professional sports career. How did you get started?

DOUG: I guess I was always interested in sports. Any game was worth the effort for me. During high school, I was in football, basketball and track and field. I liked to compete.

DEBBIE: How do athletes get "discovered"?

DOUG: There are scouts in all sports. These people watch young players and report back to their home teams. Many scouts came to see me. I had several offers to play football at university. I had four great years at the University of Cincinatti. After I finished school, I signed to play for Ottawa.

DEBBIE: Have you played other sports as well as football?

DOUG: I almost became a pro basketball player once. Many successful athletes have played more than one sport.

DEBBIE: You played eight years of football for a living and played four years at university before that. That's a long time at one job.

DOUG: Well, for many people, four years is often a whole career, especially in football!

DEBBIE: If you work hard at sports are you always sure of success?

DOUG: Not always. The competition is really tough. And sometimes an athlete may suffer a slump in his or her game for a while.

DEBBIE: What are the drawbacks to being a pro athlete?

DOUG: Training camp can be hard. You have to stay in top form.

DEBBIE: Did you have many injuries when you were playing?

DOUG: I've had quite a few injuries. My nose has been broken twice; I have several scars from being kicked in games. But I guess my worst injury was to my right clavicle.

DEBBIE: I don't even know what a clavicle is.

DOUG: The clavicle—that's the collar bone. I had to have my right clavicle removed in an operation. Both my legs have had badly torn ligaments. I even had ligament transplants. Maybe you might call my knees bionic!

DEBBIE: Tell us about the good side of an athlete's life.

DOUG: Well, it's never just a job. You travel and meet all sorts of interesting people. There's plenty of friendship and teamwork.

DEBBIE: Were sports good for you as a person?

DOUG: I think so, Debbie. Sports gave me determination. I "grew" as a person. I became more understanding of other people.

DEBBIE: Now you're a school teacher. Was that always an ambition?

DOUG: I planned to become a teacher when I went to university. Most athletes plan to have a second career. No one can play forever!

DEBBIE: When you think back to the Grey Cup games you played, what do you like to remember?

DOUG: The 1973 Grey Cup game stands out for me. The Edmonton Eskimos with their gold and green colours and Ottawa with their red, white and black brightened the field. But we weren't feeling very bright when we first ran out onto the field! You see, at the start of that game, Edmonton was the favourite.

DEBBIE: What part of the game do you remember best?

DOUG: I had some good luck. An Edmonton player fumbled the ball. I managed to see a hole in the crowd of players. I went in, grabbed the ball and took it out of play. This resulted in a forty yard advantage for Ottawa. We finally won the game 22 to 18.

DEBBIE: I can see why you'd remember that one! What advice would you give young people who are interested in sports?

DOUG: Always try your best. Enjoy the sports you play. You might never get to be a professional but you can have a lot of fun as an amateur!

One Good Turn

Dennis Pelrine

The supermarket parking lot looked very different
that Sunday. There were motorcycle police officers
there to make sure that no cars would get in the
way. The fire fighters had just finished chalking
white lines to mark the course. There were some
adults standing around.

Mostly though, the crowd was made up of boys and girls about eight or nine years old. All of them had skateboards and that wasn't really strange, because it was the day of Lethbridge's first skateboard race.

Everyone was hoping that the weather would get better. Towards the west, there were some big dark clouds that looked to be full of rain.

"If those clouds move this way," said one of the parents, "we'll have a swimming race instead of a skateboard race."

While the fire fighters checked the course to make sure that everything was right, the wind began to blow some of the dark clouds away.

As the boys and girls waited for the call to the starting line, they talked about who was likely to win. Some thought Jim would be hard to beat. Others picked Angie, because she could make sharp turns without losing her balance. Both had done very well in the semi-finals.

"Forget it," Peter told them. "Rollie is going to win because he's the biggest and toughest of all."

"But that has nothing to do with it," Tracey told him. "In skateboarding, it's being fast and smart that counts."

"Not this time," Peter said. "Rollie has a plan. He's going to bump anyone who starts to pass him."

"But that's dirty," Jim protested.

"So what," said Rollie. "You see lots of bumping and hitting in hockey. That's how you make sure you win."

"Well, I don't know about that," Buffey told him. "But in this game, you win by using your head, not by being dirty!"

"You do it your way. I'll do it mine," Rollie said, looking very sure of himself.

"I think you're wrong, Rollie," Tracey said. "Besides, it's not worth it, anyway."

"What do you mean?" Rollie asked, and he wasn't grinning any longer.

"Well, it's like this," Peter told him. "Do you like having friends?"

"Of course. I have lots of friends."

"You may have right now," Tracey told Rollie, "but one little bump and you won't have *any* friends left!"

"Besides, you don't need to skate dirty," said Angie. "You're bigger and stronger than the rest of us."

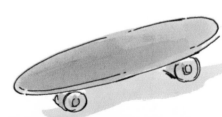

"That won't help," Rollie said, looking sad. "I can go fast down the straight stretches, but I can't make those sharp turns. If I try them going fast, I fall off every time."

"That's because when you make turns, you stand up too straight," Tracey said.

Putting one foot on her board, Tracey rolled away from the group, turned, picked up speed and came zooming back toward them. Just when it seemed she was going to crash into them, she made a perfect sharp turn at full speed, then came to a stop and jumped off.

"You see?" she said to Rollie. "It's easy. You have to bend your knees and lean into the turn. That way you have better balance. Go on, give it a try."

He built up speed as he came back toward the group, but he looked worried.

"Crouch down, Rollie," Tracey called to him. "It's easy."

Rollie crouched and went into the turn. His board tipped and he flew off. Luckily, he landed on his feet, but he wasn't pleased.

"You see?" he said to Tracey. "I did just what you said and it didn't work."

"That's because you were too tight. You have to relax, stay loose," Tracey told him. Then she showed him again how she did it.

"All contestants come to the starting line!" a man called, and the boys and girls picked up their boards and hurried away.

"Quick, Rollie," Tracey told the boy. "Do it one more time. Stay loose. You'll see how easy it is."

Remembering what she had told him, he crouched and tried to loosen up. As he went into the turn, he caught his breath, almost closed his eyes, and then he heard Tracey shouting.

"You did it," she called. "Come on, let's catch up with the others."

Tracey and Rollie ran to the line and were both out of breath when they got there. The man who was starting the race noticed that. In order to give them time to catch their breath, he took some papers out of his pocket and pretended to read them for a while.

"Everybody ready?" he shouted. "On your mark . . . get set . . . GO!"

The crowd cheered as the skaters took off down the course.

As they neared the first turn, Rollie and Jim were slightly ahead. Tracey was third and Helena was fourth. At the turn, Rollie slowed a little. When they went into the second turn, Tracey was leading with Jim close behind.

As the racers neared the next turn, Rollie told himself he had to take a chance. Squatting down, he remembered what Tracey had shown him. He went into the turn at full speed and when he came out of it, he and Tracey were racing side by side.

There were still two turns to go in the race and as Tracey and Rollie neared the next one, they heard another board coming up fast. Both Rollie and Tracey made the turn perfectly, but so did the third board. It was Jim, and he was gaining on them.

Just then a dog chased a cat through the crowd. The cat ran right out onto the course with the dog following. The cat managed to get across the track, but the dog got in Jim's way.

Jim went straight up in the air. his board shot between the dog's legs and Jim came down on the seat of his pants. Other racers shot past him, but everybody saw that the winner would be Tracey or Rollie. It was too late for the others to catch up.

"Tracey's going to win," someone shouted as the two racers went toward the final turn.

At that point, she was about the length of a skateboard ahead. Because she could make fast turns, it seemed she was going to win the race. As they reached the turn, she crouched, relaxed, and the board made a clean turn. But Rollie had made an even better turn. Coming out of it, Rollie was ahead by a bit less than the length of a board.

The rest of the race was easy—just one long, straight dash. The crowd roared as the two leaders streaked toward the finish line.

"ROLLIE IS THE WINNER," shouted the judge. "TRACEY IS SECOND."

As the others rolled across the finish line all the racers gathered in a crowd. They were out of breath, but they looked excited. It had been a great race. Even Jim joined them, holding his skateboard under his left arm and rubbing the seat of his pants with his right hand.

"Hey Rollie," said Tracey excitedly, "that was some kind of a turn you made!"

"It sure was," Rollie agreed. "Thanks for showing me how to do it."

"Hey Tracey," one of the girls called to her, "that was a big mistake you made! If you hadn't shown him how to make turns, you would have won the race."

"Big deal," said Tracey with a grin. "Winning is just what happens at the end of the race. The whole race was fun. That's what races are all about."

By that time, the parents had gathered around the boys and girls, and were telling them how exciting the race had been for them.

"Congratulations, Tracey," Rollie's mother said and put an arm around the girl's shoulders. "I saw what you did for Rollie just before the race."

"We're friends," Tracey told her. "And friends do good turns for each other."

Seeing is Believing

Shiny flying saucers?
I've never ever seen one.
A lot of people talk as if
They see them every night.
The Loch Ness Monster?
I wonder if there is one;
A lot of people say they've seen
This strange and scary sight.
Big hairy Sasquatches?
Where do people find them?
I never seem to be right there
To catch a glimpse of one.
And mischief-making leprechauns
That dance around the forest?
There's something else I haven't seen—
I'm missing *all* the fun.

I like the stories people tell;
I guess they're not deceiving.
But I want to see things for myself,
For seeing is believing.

John McInnes

Blue Moose

Manus Pinkwater

Mr. Breton had a little restaurant on the edge of the big woods. When winter came, the north wind blew through the trees and froze everything solid. Then it snowed. Mr. Breton didn't like snow.

Mr. Breton was a very good cook. Every day people from the town came to his restaurant. They ate gallons of his special clam chowder. They ate plates of his special beef stew. They ate fish stew and special homemade bread. The people from the town never talked much, and they never said anything about Mr. Breton's cooking.

"Did you like your clam chowder?" Mr. Breton would ask.

"Yup," the people from the town would say.

Mr. Breton wished they would say, "Delicious!" or "Good chowder, Breton!" All they ever said was, "Yup."

Every morning Mr. Breton went out behind his house to get firewood. He wore three sweaters, a scarf, galoshes, a woollen hat, a big checkered coat, and mittens. He still felt cold. Sometimes

raccoons and rabbits came out of the woods to watch Mr. Breton. The cold didn't bother them.

One morning there was a moose in Mr. Breton's yard. It was a blue moose. When Mr. Breton went out his back door, the moose was there, looking at him. After a while Mr. Breton went back in and made a pot of coffee while he waited for the moose to go away. It didn't go away; it just stood in Mr. Breton's yard, looking at his back door. Mr. Breton drank a cup of coffee. The moose stood in the yard. Mr. Breton opened the door again.

"Shoo! Go away!" he said to the moose.

"Do you mind if I come in and get warm?" said the moose. "I'm just about frozen." He brushed past Mr. Breton and walked into the kitchen. his antlers almost touched the ceiling. Mr. Breton stared at him.

The moose sat down on the floor next to Mr. Breton's stove. He closed his eyes and sat leaning toward the stove for a long time. Wisps of steam began to rise from his blue fur. After a long time the moose sighed. It sounded like a foghorn.

"Can I get you a cup of coffee?" Mr. Breton asked the moose. "Or some clam chowder?"

"Clam chowder," said the moose.

Mr. Breton filled a bowl with creamy clam chowder and set it on the floor. The moose dipped his big nose into the bowl and snuffled up the chowder. He made a sort of slurping, whistling noise.

"Sir," the moose said, "this is wonderful clam chowder."

Mr. Breton blushed a very deep red. "Do you really mean that?"

"Sir," the moose said, "I have eaten some very good chowder in my time, but yours is the very best."

"Oh, my," said Mr. Breton, blushing even
redder. "Oh my. Would you like some more?"

"Yes, with crackers," said the moose.

The moose ate seventeen bowls of chowder with
crackers. Then he had twelve pieces of hot
gingerbread and forty-eight cups of coffee. While
the moose slurped and whistled, Mr. Breton sat in
a chair. Every now and then he said to himself,
"Oh my. The best he's ever eaten. Oh my."

Later, when some people from the town came to Mr. Breton's house, the moose met them at the door. "How many in your party, please?" the moose asked. "I have a table for you; please follow me."

The people from the town were surprised to see the moose. They felt like running away, but they were too surprised. The moose led them to a table, brought them menus, looked at each person, snorted, and clumped into the kitchen. "There are some people outside; I'll take care of them," he told Mr. Breton.

The people were whispering to one another about the moose when he clumped back to the table. "Are you ready to order?" he asked.

"Yup," said the people from the town. They waited for the moose to ask them if they would like some chowder, the way Mr. Breton always did. But the moose just stared at them as though they were very foolish. The people felt uncomfortable. "We'll have the clam chowder."

"Chaudière aux clams; very good," the moose said. "Do you desire crackers or homemade bread?"

"We will have crackers," said the people from the town.

"I suggest you have the bread; it is hot," said the moose.

74

"We will have bread," said the people from the town.

"And for dessert," said the moose, "will you have fresh gingerbread or apple jaquette?"

"What do you recommend?" asked the people from the town.

"After the chaudière aux clams, the gingerbread is best."

"Thank you," said the people from the town.

"It is my pleasure to serve you," said the moose. He brought bowls of chowder balanced on his antlers.

At the end of the meal, the moose clumped to the table. "Has everything been to your satisfaction?"

"Yup," said the people from the town, their mouths full of gingerbread.

"I beg your pardon?" said the moose. "What did you say?"

"It was very good," said the people from the town. "It was the best we've ever eaten."

"I will tell the chef," said the moose.

The moose clumped into the kitchen and told Mr. Breton what the people from the town had said. Mr. Breton rushed out of the kitchen and out of the house. The people from the town were sitting on the porch, putting on their snowshoes. "Did you tell the moose that my clam chowder was the best you've ever eaten?" Mr. Breton asked.

"Yup," said the people from the town. "We said that. We think that you are the best cook in the world; we have always thought so."

"Always?" asked Mr. Breton.

"Of course," the people from the town said.

"Why do you think we walk seven miles on snowshoes just to eat here?"

The people from the town walked away on their snowshoes. Mr. Breton sat on the edge of the porch and thought it over. When the moose came out to see why Mr. Breton was sitting outside without his coat on, Mr. Breton said, "Do you know, those people think I am the best cook in the whole world?"

"Of course they do," the moose said. "By the way, aren't you cold out here?"

"No, I'm not the least bit cold," Mr. Breton said. "This is turning out to be a very mild winter."

When spring finally came, the moose became moody. He spent a lot of time staring out the back door. Flocks of geese flew overhead, returning to lakes in the north, and the moose always stirred when he heard their honking.

"Chef," said the moose one morning, "I will be going tomorrow. I wonder if you would pack some gingerbread for me to take along."

Mr. Breton baked a special batch of gingerbread, packed it in parcels, and tied the parcels with string so the moose could hang them from his antlers. When the moose came downstairs, Mr. Breton was sitting in the kitchen, drinking coffee. The parcels of gingerbread were on the kitchen table.

"Do you want a cup of coffee before you go?" Mr. Breton asked.

"Thank you," said the moose.

"I shall certainly miss you," Mr. Breton said.

"Thank you," said the moose.

"Do you suppose you'll ever come back?" asked Mr. Breton.

"Not before Thursday or Friday," said the moose. "It would be impolite to visit my uncle for less than a week." The moose hooked his antlers into the loops of string on the parcels of

gingerbread. "My uncle will like this." He stood up and turned toward the door.

"Wait!" Mr. Breton shouted. "Do you mean that you are not leaving forever? I thought you were lonely for the life of a wild moose. I thought you wanted to go back to the wild free places."

"Chef, do you have any idea how cold it gets in the wild free places?" the moose said. "And the food! Terrible!"

"Have a nice time at your uncle's," said Mr. Breton.

"I'll send you a postcard," said the moose.

Supertalk Calling Milkman

Dennis Pelrine

"What's this?" Frank asked as he picked up the thing he had found in the milk box of his apartment.

It was black and shiny and had some chrome on it. It looked very much like a radio, Frank thought. But who would put a radio in the milk box? Frank jerked the door open and looked up and down the long hall of the seventh floor. Nothing. Not a person in sight. Not a sound.

"But this is crazy," Frank said and shook his head. "Nobody would put a brand new radio in our milk box just for fun."

When he opened the milk box again and looked carefully, Frank found a piece of paper with some writing on it. He began to read the note.

"I have two
But one will do.
Listen a lot,
You may get a clue."

The strange note was signed "Supertalk".

"Let me see now," Frank said aloud as he walked to the dining room table where he sat. "I have two but one will do." He thought about the words.

"I know. Somebody gave him two radios," he decided. "He can't use two radios at the same time so he gave one to me. No, that doesn't make sense," Frank added, and then began to examine the radio.

The chrome thing on top turned out to be an antenna, so he pulled it out as far as it would go.

"Now I know," Frank said, excited. "It's not just a radio. It's a walkie-talkie!"

Frank turned the knob on the side and there was a rush of noise from it.

"What are you doing, Frank?" his sister called from the kitchen.

"I'm not sure, not really," Frank answered as his older sister Sandy came into the room to see.

"Where did you get the walkie-talkie?" Sandy asked. Frank told her and then showed her the note.

"Do you understand the poem, Frank?" she asked.

"Sure," he told her, and explained what he had figured out.

"Your're right," Sandy told her brother. "A walkie-talkie is a lot like a CB radio, but you use it for shorter distances."

Sandy went on to explain about CB radios to her brother. She told how CB radio users give themselves names and speak in a strange code.

"How do you know all that?" Frank asked?

"Because I'm so grown up and smart," Sandy said and shrugged; then she laughed. "You know my friend Inez? Her whole family is into CB radio. I learned it all from them. I even know most of the code."

Just as Frank was about to ask his sister what that meant, the sound of a voice made him jump.

"Threes, Milkman. Back."

Frank blinked as he looked at the walkie-talkie.

"Who was that?" he asked.

"I think that was your mystery friend," Sandy told her brother. "Listen. *Threes* means hello," she went on. "*Milkman* is a name he gave you because you found the unit in the milk box. *Back* means over to you. Here, I'll tell you what to say."

Frank pressed the talk button, and started saying the words his sister wrote for him.

"Threes and nines," he said into the walkie-talkie. "This is Milkman. What's your handle? Give a shout."

"Hey Sandy, what does it all mean? I guess *give a shout* means call me back, but what about *handle*?" Frank asked his sister.

"Handle is his name. When he called you Milkman, that was your handle."

"Hey there, good buddy Milkman," came the voice from the walkie-talkie. My handle is Supertalk. 10—3."

"What do all those numbers mean?" Frank asked as he heard his sister laugh loudly.

"10—3 means that's all for now," explained Sandy. He doesn't want you to call him back now."

"I'll never be able to learn all this," Frank said as he looked at the walkie-talkie.

"Sure you will, Frank," his big sister told him and mussed up his hair. "I'll help you all you want. You're smart. You can learn the code and everything else. In no time at all, you'll be talking like a truck driver."

"I hope so. What does *Rubber Duck* mean?" Frank wanted to know. "That's somebody's name—isn't it?"

"It's more than just that," Sandy explained. When a bunch of trucks are driving in a convoy— you know, a whole line of them—the driver of the front truck is called Rubber Duck."

Frank wasn't so sure that he was going to be able to learn the code, but he made up his mind to give it a good try.

He would hurry home from school each day for another talk with Supertalk. He had no idea what his mystery friend's real name was or where he lived. He often asked him, but Supertalk always laughed and told him to find out for himself.

"I'll give you a clue, good buddy," Supertalk told Frank one day. "I live high up in a square mountain."

Frank worked on that for a while and it just didn't make sense. Next day, as he was walking home from school, Frank looked up at the apartment building in which he lived.

"A square mountain!" he shouted in surprise and began running. Now he knew his friend lived in his building.

Not wanting to wait for Supertalk's call, Frank tried to call his friend. He tried five different times before Supertalk answered and admitted that Frank had found the answer to the riddle.

That day, they pretended they were truck drivers. Supertalk taught Milkman some new words from the code. Frank learned that a school bus is called a *blinkin' winkin'*, that a flat tire is called a *blown doughnut* and when Supertalk said, "there's a big dog heading your way, good buddy," Frank found out that a *big dog* means a Greyhound bus.

But Supertalk was still a mystery. Since he lived in the same apartment, Frank felt sure he went to the same school. He listened to voices at school carefully, but none sounded at all like Supertalk.

In his apartment building, Frank spent a lot of time around the lobby. Each time he saw a boy around his own age whom he didn't know, Frank would speak to him and listen carefully to the voice that replied. It was always the same. The voice never sounded like Supertalk.

"Darn it, Sandy," Frank told his sister one day, "I wish he'd tell me his name and where he lives."

"I guess he must have a reason, Frank," she said. "Why not settle for having him as a good walkie-talkie friend?"

"But that's just it," Frank protested. "We have such fun when we talk. We play games. We pretend to be different people. I can tell by his voice that he's a nice guy. I'd like him to be my friend all the time, not just on the walkie-talkie."

"Try to be patient," Sandy said, and then she went to do her homework.

Suddenly a loud voice came from his walkie-talkie:

"MAYDAY . . . MILKMAN . . . FRANK . . . HELP . . ."

Frank knew that the word *Mayday* meant trouble, a real emergency. His friend's tone was serious. He was in some kind of trouble. Sandy noticed it too and hurried to her brother.

"Where are you, Supertalk?" Frank asked.

"Apartment 808. Right over your head. Hurry!"

Still holding the walkie-talkie, Frank ran toward the door, telling his friend he was on his way. In the hall, Frank ran toward the doorway to the stairs and heard his sister right behind him. They went up the stairs fast. They saw the apartment door and saw a bit of smoke coming out under it.

"Call the fire department," Sandy shouted to a woman who had just got off the elevator.

Frank didn't bother to knock. He turned the knob and pushed the door open wide. A lot of smoke came out, but it didn't stop him.

Inside the apartment, he saw that the smoke seemed to be blowing out in a stream from the kitchen. The rest of the room was pretty clear.

"In here, Frank," Supertalk called. "In the kitchen. Help me!"

Frank ran to the kitchen with his sister.

"My mom's hurt. We have to get her out of here," the boy said, pointing to the woman who lay on the floor.

At the same time that Frank saw the woman, he saw Supertalk. He was sitting in a wheelchair.

Frank and his sister crouched down beside the woman. They saw her eyes open, and she moved a little.

"Jim," the woman called as her eyes opened wide and she saw the smoke. "Are you all right?"

"Yes, Mom, I'm right here," the boy in the wheelchair said. "My friends are helping us."

"Call the fire department," the woman said as Frank and Sandy helped her to stand.

"Somebody is already doing that," Frank told the woman; then they agreed that they should get out of the apartment.

The woman could walk fairly well, Frank saw, so while his sister helped her get through the smoke and out the door, Frank pushed Supertalk's wheelchair.

Around them, they heard excited people, but Frank and Supertalk and Sandy and the boy's mother were quite calm. The smoke made them cough quite a lot, but now they were outside in the hall and it wasn't so bad there.

The firemen came, and after a few minutes one of them came out and told the people that there was nothing to worry about.

"You can go back to your apartments," he told them in a loud voice. "It was just the electric stove. The building isn't on fire."

"I was fixing the thing," Supertalk's mother told one of the firemen. "I felt the shock and that's all I know."

"It threw her right across the room," Supertalk told the others. "She bumped her head on that wall, and then a curtain caught fire."

"I'm all right, dear," the woman said and rubbed her son's head. "Thanks for getting your friends here so fast."

"What's wrong with your legs?" Frank asked Supertalk.

"My legs don't work too well. I guess they were short of the right pieces when I was being made," he said and grinned at his joke.

"I'm sorry, Supertalk," Frank told him. "Gee, I don't know what to say. Oh, this is my sister Sandy. We live in 708."

"I know, Frank. I'm the one who put the walkie-talkie in your milk box."

"I'm sure glad you did, but why did you pick me?"

"Because your friend Supertalk heard you talking out on your balcony," said Jim's mother. "He liked your voice. He said he wished you were his friend. You're the first person he's ever said that about."

"I'm glad, Jim," Frank told his friend. "We can play together a lot."

"I'm not very good at playing," Jim told him and looked a little sad.

"Are you kidding?" asked Frank. "Look, when we use our walkie-talkies and play truck driver games, you've got wheels, real wheels."

"That's true," Jim agreed and he seemed to cheer up.

"There are so many things we could do," Frank told him as both boys became excited. "We could go out to the park to play. I could push your chair."

92

"How nice of you, Frank," the boy's mother said
and smiled. "Since Jim is ready to make friends
now and get around, I think he's ready for a
motorized chair so he can drive himself."

"Neat-O!" Frank shouted.

Soon, Jim got his new chair with a motor. He
and Frank spent a lot of time playing in the park.
Frank brought his bike, Jim drove his chair, and it
made playing truck driver very real.

The Golden Key

Wayne Carley

Do you believe in ghosts? Barry Clarkson didn't. At least he didn't on the day he first saw the MacTaggart summer house on the Bay of Fundy.

Barry was staying with his grandparents. They

worked for the MacTaggarts. They did the cleaning and cooking and gardening.

Every year Barry's grandparents came down from the city to open the summer house. They always came a week early. They worked very hard. They made sure that the water and electricity were working. They aired out the rooms. They cleaned and polished the furniture. Then, a week later, when the MacTaggarts arrived everything was ready. It was as though the house had not stood alone and empty all winter long.

This was the first year that Barry came with them. It was supposed to be a summer holiday for him, but he knew the real reason he was there. He was there to be a playmate for the MacTaggart's son. Barry didn't like the idea very much.

It was raining on the day they arrived. Barry's grandfather steered the car off the road into what looked like a park. As far as you could see there was nothing but lawn and trees.

Barry knew that the summer house wouldn't be a shack, but he was surprised at the size of the house he saw. It was huge. It was made out of wood that the weather had turned grey. The windows, with their trims painted white, looked out to sea. They looked like big, unblinking eyes.

"Gee," Barry whispered. Then he asked, "How many rooms does it have?"

His grandmother laughed. "I don't know," she said. "I've never bothered to count them. But the whole third floor is shut off. And that's fine with me. Keeping the first two floors clean is hard enough work."

Barry looked up at the third floor. "I wonder what's up there?" he thought to himself.

"Come on," said Barry's grandfather as he opened the car door. "We've got a lot of work to do. Let's get busy."

The next few days were busy for Barry's grandparents but not for Barry. He just seemed to get in the way. His grandparents finally told him to go play on the beach. So Barry did. But it wasn't much fun playing alone.

Then his grandparents suggested that he start a shell collection. So Barry took a big burlap sack to the beach and started filling it with shells. In a couple of days the sack was nearly full. And Barry still wasn't having much fun.

One morning Barry headed for the beach again. He sighed. "I might as well go back to my shell collection," he thought to himself. "Except if I collect many more I'll need a truck to get them home."

The burlap sack was just where he had left it. He undid the string at the top and looked in. Suddenly, he dropped to his knees in surprise.

There on top of the shells lay a key. A shiny, gold key that flashed in the sunshine. It was big and very old fashioned. It had a large, round handle on one end. Barry sat back on his heels.

"Well, how did that get there?" he asked himself.

Barry took the key and headed back up to the house. His grandparents were washing windows. They both just glanced at the key when Barry showed it to them.

His grandmother said, "I've never seen it before. Just leave it in the kitchen and we'll ask the MacTaggarts about it when they arrive."

"I'd like to hold on to it for a while," Barry said. "Maybe I can find the door that it opens."

His grandmother laughed. "Okay," she said. "But don't get into any trouble."

Barry started his search. He found that on the first two floors most of the doors didn't even have locks. And those that did, had new locks. The key was much too old fashioned to fit them. Then Barry remembered the third floor. But he didn't know how to get up there.

Barry checked the whole second floor looking for a stairway up. But there didn't seem to be one. Then, at the end of the hall, he found a door that had been wallpapered over to look like the rest of the wall. There was no key hole in the door.

At first he thought the door wouldn't open. But it was just stuck. He pulled and pulled and with a loud, long creak the door opened. Barry saw a dark stairway leading up to the third floor.

"Here we go," thought Barry. He started up the stairs.

He stood on the third floor and looked at the rows of doors. "Which one is it?" he wondered.

But he didn't need a key. Door after door was unlocked. The rooms he found were empty and dusty. Cobwebs hung in the windows. In one room, a bat flashed through the air nearly hitting Barry in the face. He closed that door in a hurry. Then he found a door that was locked.

He put his ear to the door. He didn't feel like meeting any more bats. But all was quiet on the other side. He put the key in the lock. It turned easily. Slowly and quietly he pushed the door open.

Unlike the others, this room was clean and shiny. It had furniture. There was a window seat that looked out over the sea. There were two desks that faced each other. One was large, like a teacher's desk. The other was small, as though built for a child. On one wall there was a blackboard with writing on it. The writing said:

I will not mock my tutor.
I will not mock my tutor.

Over and over again the words were written.

In the middle of the floor, Barry saw two armies of toy soldiers lined up for battle. One army wore red. The other army wore blue. Many of the soldiers were on horseback. They held swords.

Suddenly, a voice said, "The battle is about to start. Which side do you want?"

Barry jumped. He wheeled around and saw a boy standing near the window seat.

The boy was about Barry's age. But there was something strange about him. For one thing, his clothes were strange. He wore a white shirt with big sleeves and a ruffled collar. His pants were tucked into long blue socks that came up to his knees. His shoes had big buckles on them.

But it wasn't just his clothes that made him strange. Barry found it hard to look at him. It was as though the boy's face was passing through shadows. At one moment it would be light. Then it would go dark. But the scary thing was that the light wasn't coming from the window. It seemed to be coming from inside the boy himself.

Barry felt cold. Suddenly he really was scared.

"Hey, what's going on here?" Barry said. "Who are you and how did you get in here?"

The boy answered, "I am James MacTaggart. And I have met you before."

"No, you haven't," answered Barry.

"Do not argue with me," the boy said. "You are just a servant here and I am the young master of the house. If I say we have met before, then it is true."

"You're crazy," said Barry. "I'm getting out of here!"

"Come back!" the boy called. "We haven't had the battle yet."

Barry stopped at the door. "What battle?" he asked.

The boy pointed to the toy soldiers. He picked two of them up.

"This is General Teddington," he said, holding up a soldier in red. Then he held out the soldier in blue. "And this is General Bullyboy. He always wins. I will have the blue army, of course."

Barry ran toward the door.

"I've got to get out of here!" he cried.

As he ran down the hall he heard a door close behind him. Then he heard a key turn in a lock. He remembered that he had left the key in the room with the boy.

Barry ran down all three flights of stairs. His grandparents were still washing windows.

Barry told them about the room and finding the boy. His grandfather ran toward the stairway.

"It's probably just some kid from the neighbourhood who somehow got in the house. I'll go see what's going on," he said.

"I'll get the master key," Barry's grandmother said. "We'll need it if the door is locked."

Barry and his grandparents ran to the door on the third floor. It was locked. His grandfather took the master key and put it in the lock. He twisted the key back and forth but nothing happened.

It's no good," Barry's grandfather said. "This lock is too old. The master key won't work."

"Let me try," Barry said.

Barry took the master key and put it in the lock. The key turned easily and the lock clicked open.

"Now how did you do that?" Barry's grandfather asked. "It certainly wouldn't work for me."

Barry pushed the door open. As he stood staring into the room he felt his grandmother come up behind him. "Oh, Barry," she whispered.

The window seat was still there. And the two desks. But everything was covered with inches of heavy, grey dust. Huge cobwebs hung from the ceiling. The toy soldiers lay on the floor. They were almost buried in dust. Their uniforms were tarnished and black.

Barry's grandmother said, "How on earth did you find this room? It looks like it hasn't been used in a hundred years."

"But I was just in it," Barry said. "And it wasn't like this. It was all clean and shiny!"

"Barry, you couldn't have been in here," his grandfather said.

"But I was! I was!" Barry cried.

"Look at the dust on the floor. There are no footprints. Nobody has walked in this room for years," Barry's grandfather said.

"Come along," said Barry's grandmother. "Let's just close the door and leave the room alone."

Barry took one more look at the room. He noticed the blackboard. The words "I will not mock my tutor" had been erased. Now there were only two words on the blackboard. They said:

UNTIL TOMORROW

Barry slept badly that night. He kept having the same dream. In his dream he could see the room. The boy was in it. Over and over again, he kept holding two toy soldiers out to Barry.

The next morning the MacTaggarts were going to arrive. Barry wanted to be with his grandparents to meet them.

Barry stood with his grandparents on the steps of the house. A big, black car moved silently up the driveway. It stopped in front of the house.

Barry's grandfather opened the back door of the car. A man stepped out. It was Mr. MacTaggart.

"Good morning, Clarkson," Mr. MacTaggart said to Barry's grandfather. "I hope the house is ready."

"Everything is quite ready, sir," said Barry's grandfather.

"Good. Good," Mr. MacTaggart said. He looked around and spotted Barry on the steps. "This must be your grandson. Come here, boy. I want you to meet your new friend," he called to Barry.

Barry walked slowly down the steps. He saw that someone was sitting in the back of the car.

Mr. MacTaggart said, "Come along now, boys. I want you to introduce yourselves."

Barry looked in the car. Then he took a step back.

Sitting in the back of the car was the boy Barry had met in the room yesterday. The boy's clothes were different. But the face was exactly the same. The same cold, blue eyes. The same voice when he spoke.

"I am James MacTaggart the fifth," the boy said, "and I have met you before."

Barry felt weak.

The boy went on, "And I believe you also know a couple of my friends, General Teddington and General Bullyboy. As you know, General Bullyboy always wins."

Barry looked at the two toy soldiers being held out to him. They were the same as the ones he had seen yesterday. He saw their shiny uniforms. He saw the tiny medals on their chests. And he saw the boy's cold, blue eyes, and his cold smile.

A Fish Tale

Ella Manuel

A long time ago, on the coast of Newfoundland, a woman named Elizabeth married a fisherman called William. They went to live in a little house on the rocks of Herring Harbour.

William and Elizabeth were very poor. They had only a little furniture and few dishes because they were just getting started in life. Still, they were happy.

Elizabeth and William would help each other clean and split the codfish, then put them out to dry in the sun. Both Elizabeth and William looked forward to earning enough money to buy what they needed for their house.

Early that summer William said, "Let's start a list of what we really need and another list of what we would like if we have enough money left over. We'll go to St. John's and sell a boat-load of dry fish."

We'll need a lot of fish," said Elizabeth, looking down at the *Daisy* tied to the wharf below the house. "We'll have to take someone with us, too. Those big sails are heavy and it's a long way to St. John's."

William replied, "It would take us about five days, if the wind is right. The *Daisy* is fast and steady. We'll see some fine places when we anchor at night! I'll get someone to go with us. You dry the fish and figure out how we'll spend all that money we get when we sell it. We'll get the best prices going. I'm sure of it."

Every day, William would go out with a crew of two (plus a cook) and fish about thirty kilometres off shore. The cod were large and plentiful there. After three or four days, they would sail back and unload their catch. Elizabeth would split and clean the fish and spread them flat on the rocks of the beach. The families of the other two crew members would help. Several times a day they turned the fish over. When the sun went down, they piled the fish neatly and covered them with canvas to protect them against dew or rain showers. It was hard work, but in the sunshine and cool breezes, everyone enjoyed it.

That summer, the sun shone for weeks on end.

The pile of dried codfish grew larger every day. Then one day, clouds came and filled the sky. For two days the Herring Harbour people did not even get a peep of the sun. All the people collected the half-dry fish and stored them in their sheds. They hoped their fish wouldn't rot before the sun came again. Then it rained. The wind howled and the sea banged the boats against the rocks. All the people were busy trying to save what they could from the boats.

One morning after a week of storms, William came into the kitchen. Water was pouring off his oilskins. While he removed his boots, he said to Elizabeth: "I guess we won't get that boatload of fish after all. The fish won't dry in time."

Elizabeth said quietly, "How much more fish do we need to make a load for the *Daisy?*"

"About twice as much as we have now," replied William. "The wind is dying back so we'll be off in an hour for the fishing grounds. We may not be back for a couple of days."

Elizabeth began to gather food and extra socks for William. All the time she was thinking hard. After she kissed William good-bye, she said, "I suppose I can get young Jim down to help. If the sun comes out, he can help me put out the fish." As soon as the *Daisy* had left the wharf,

Elizabeth put on her rubber boots and thick
sweater. She walked down over the slippery rocks
to the shed where the fish and gear were stored.
She unlocked the door and stepped into the
dimness. In five minutes, she was out again,
carrying two heavy coils of rope, one over each
arm. She slowly climbed to her house and put the
rope on the floor of the back porch. Next, she
went into the little shed behind the house and
brought out a large hammer, a box of nails and a
step-ladder. She took the tools into the house and
left them in the porch. Then she got an axe, and
began to split some logs into small pieces. Soon
Elizabeth had an enormous pile of kindling.

As she came around the corner of the house, she
saw young Jim going home from the shop. She
called to him. "I want you to help me," she said.
"If I tell you what I'm going to do, will you keep
it a secret?"

Jim looked surprised. "Well, I suppose I will,"
he said. "What are you thinking about?"

"Oh, I've got a great idea. It sounds a bit
strange but I think it will work," said Elizabeth.

So Elizabeth told Jim what she was planning. He
stared at her. Then he laughed. They both laughed.
They laughed so hard their sides hurt and their
cheeks were wet with tears. Then Jim caught his
breath.

"Oh my, I'm late," he cried. "Mom will kill me if I'm not back soon. I'll see you tomorrow morning after breakfast."

That night Elizabeth slept like a log. By breakfast time she had filled all the boxes in the house with wood. She was waiting at the door for Jim when he arrived, still laughing.

They began to work, first in the kitchen. Jim climbed the ladder in the corner of the room, and hammered a nail high up in the wall. Then he tied the end of the rope firmly to the nail. He moved to the opposite corner and did the same thing. Back and forth he went, until the ceiling was criss-crossed with lines of rope. Elizabeth made sure the ropes were tight.

"That looks good," said Elizabeth. "Now let's try it out."

The two went quickly to the shed and loaded up with wet soggy salt cod. They carried the load of fish up to the kitchen. Then they got out a box of clothes pins and pinned each fish by its tail to the ropes.

The rope held. Each fish hung limp and dripping. The kitchen looked like an upside-down underwater world.

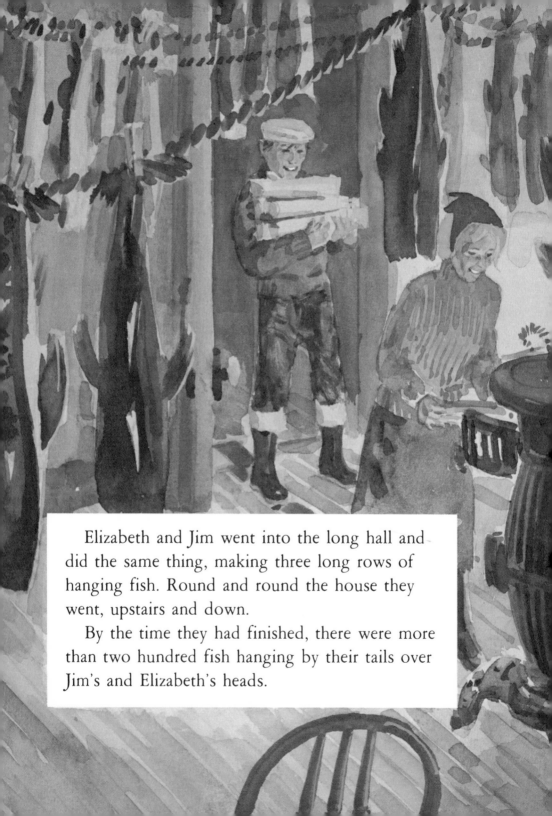

Elizabeth and Jim went into the long hall and
did the same thing, making three long rows of
hanging fish. Round and round the house they
went, upstairs and down.

By the time they had finished, there were more
than two hundred fish hanging by their tails over
Jim's and Elizabeth's heads.

"Now for the stoves!" said Elizabeth.

Though they were tired, they brought arm loads
of wood into the house. They put a pile by each of
the stoves in the house. Then they lit fires in the
stoves.

Soon the house was so hot they could hardly
breathe. But still they filled the stoves with the
good, dry wood. The windows were covered with
steam, and the walls were dripping water. Finally
Elizabeth opened the doors for half an hour. And
so they worked through the day. By nightfall the
fish were almost dry.

"We'll leave the fish hanging up tonight so that
they finish drying," said Elizabeth. "Then tomorrow
we'll put up a new batch."

Before the second batch was dry, the *Daisy* sailed back into Herring Harbour. Elizabeth and Jim were so busy they didn't notice. Suddenly the back door opened, and William walked right into a half-dry codfish. He sat down on the bench and looked around him in a daze. Elizabeth came to see who was at the door. When she saw William's face, she began to laugh. Jim heard her laughing and came to share the joke. So all three began to laugh till tears rolled down their cheeks.

"What, what, what are you doing?" sputtered William.

"Drying cod," said Jim and Elizabeth at once.

"We're getting a boatload ready to take to St. John's," chuckled Elizabeth.

"What a crazy idea!" said William shaking his head.

"Well, if drying the rest of the cod is crazy, then Jim and I are a couple of nuts," said Elizabeth. Then she explained what they had done.

William examined the piles of newly-dried cod. Then he weighed the piles and decided they would just about make up a load.

So one week later, with all the dry salt cod stored in *Daisy's* hold, and with young Jim as crew, they sailed down the coast to St. John's.

They sold the fish for a good price, and had a great time buying all the things on Elizabeth's list. They bought a new felt hat for Jim, too, with a small red feather in the band. They also bought five dozen clothes pins—in case they ever needed them again.

STAMPS TALK

Stamps can talk.
What can they tell you?

Stamps can tell you
about your own
country.

Stamps tell you
about faraway
places too.

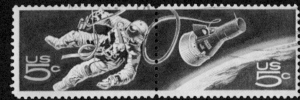

They tell you about events . . .

JULY 4, 1776

. . . and famous people.

On stamps you'll see people at work, at school and at play.

Stamps can tell you about what other children read.

Nature is a favourite subject.

You'll see trees and animals, birds and fish—even bumblebees.

You can collect stamps around your special interest or hobby.

Stamps can talk. They have a lot to say!

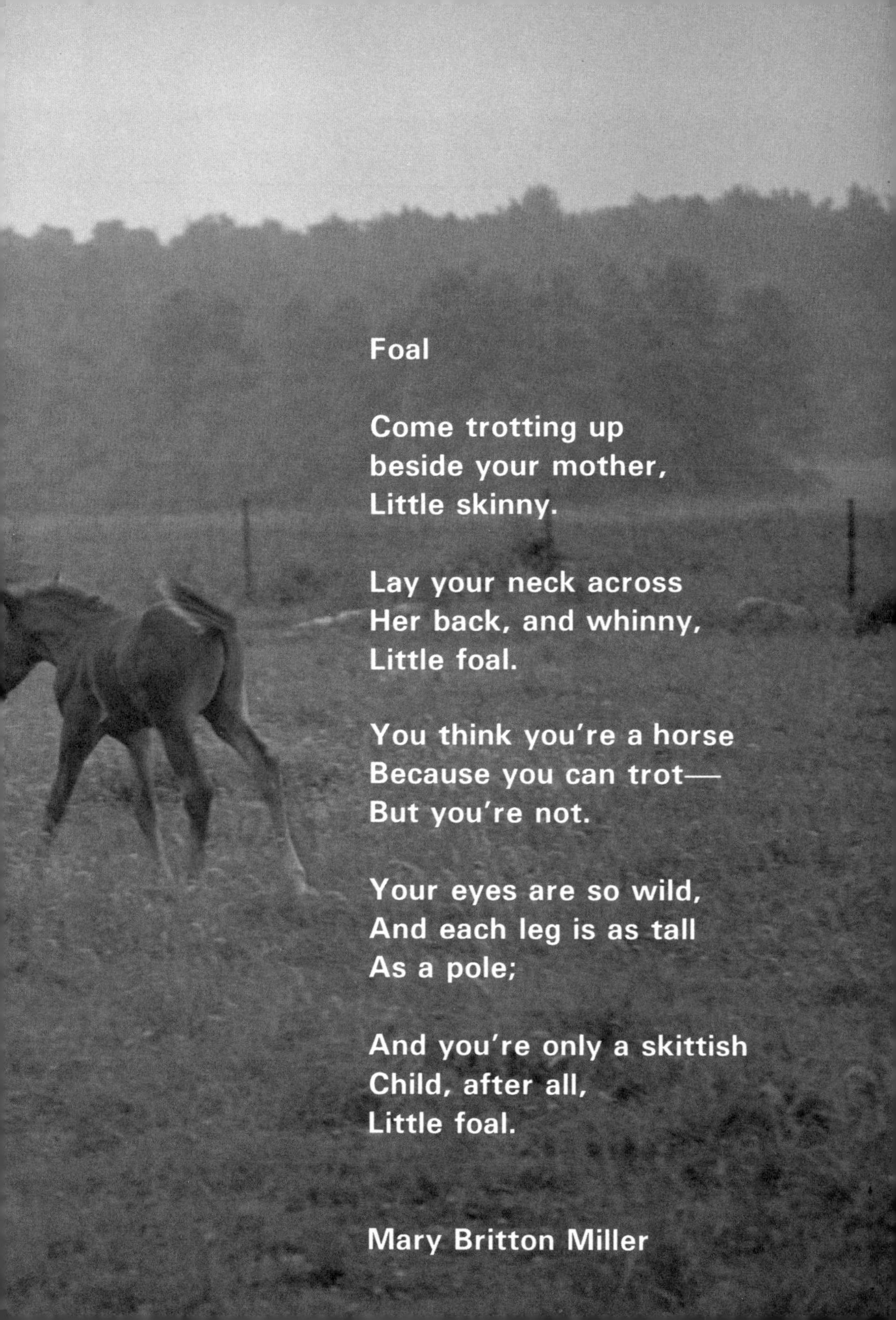

Foal

Come trotting up
beside your mother,
Little skinny.

Lay your neck across
Her back, and whinny,
Little foal.

You think you're a horse
Because you can trot—
But you're not.

Your eyes are so wild,
And each leg is as tall
As a pole;

And you're only a skittish
Child, after all,
Little foal.

Mary Britton Miller

All About Horses

Clay Graves

Appaloosa

The appaloosa is a speedy horse with a friendly manner. The front part of the appaloosa's body may be any colour. Sometimes the back part has white spots.

Arabian or Arab

Arabian horses are the oldest breed. Some people think that Arabians are the smartest horses.

Bit

The part of the bridle that goes into the horse's mouth is called the bit. It is usually made of metal, but some bits are made of nylon or rubber.

Bridle

The bridle goes over the horse's head and attaches to the bit.

Colt

A colt is what you call a male horse until he is five years old. Then you call him a horse.

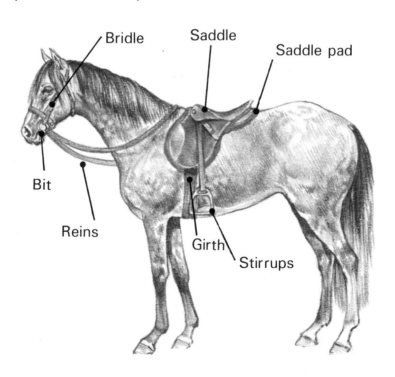

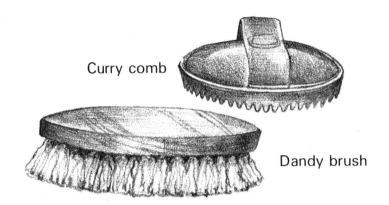

Curry comb

Dandy brush

Curry comb
The curry comb is used to clean the dandy brushes and body brushes. It looks more like a brush than a comb. The teeth on a curry comb can be metal, rubber or plastic.

Dandy brush and body brush
These brushes make the horse's coat smooth and shiny.

Filly
This is what you call a female horse that is not more than five years old. Then you call her a mare.

Foal
Any baby horse can be called a foal. A foal can stand up as soon as it is born.

Girth

The girth is the strap which holds the saddle on. It is fastened under the horse's belly.

Hackamore

A hackamore is a bridle without a bit. It is made of leather. Some horses like hackamores better than regular bridles that have bits.

Halter

A halter is a leather strap or rope which goes around the horse's head. You can hook another rope onto the halter and lead the horse around.

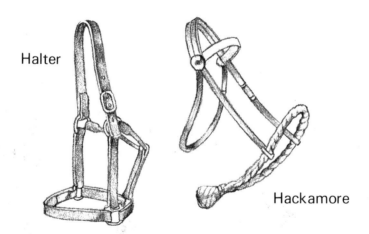

Halter

Hackamore

Hands

Horses and ponies are measured for height by number of "hands" from the ground to the top of their shoulders. A hand is about ten centimetres.

Palomino

Palominos are cream to gold coloured horses.
Their manes and tails are white.

Palomino

Pinto

Pinto

Pintos are partly white with spots of another colour. The spots must be large for the horse to be a pinto.

Pony

A pony is a small breed of horse.

Quarter horse

A quarter horse can race a quarter of a mile (about four hundred metres) very quickly. That is how it gets its name.

Reins

Reins are the leather straps you use to control a horse. You move the reins in different ways if you want a horse to stop, turn, or go slowly.

Saddle pad

This is a blanket put underneath the saddle to protect the horse's back.

Stirrups

You put your feet in the stirrups when you sit in the saddle.

Tack

Tack means the things you need for your horse, such as a saddle, a bridle, and a saddle pad.

Yearling

A yearling is a horse that is one year old.

The Present

Jo Currie

"Come on, Beth. Let's go down and feed the animals now. You can help with the horses. Here's your coat. Where did you leave your snowboots?"

Beth giggled. It was funny to have David looking after her so carefully. Usually he was just like most older brothers. He ignored her.

Their father had gone away that morning. He had to drive many miles away, to look after an old uncle who was very ill. He had been worried about leaving them alone overnight, even though David, twelve years old, had been helping with the farm

work for two years. Beth's and David's mother had
died when Beth was a baby, and Beth could not
remember a time when her father had not been
there.

"Be a good girl, Beth," their father had said,
kissing her goodbye. "If you've been specially
good, I'll buy you a present—something you really
want."

Beth had been as good and helpful as she could.
She and David had shared the barn chores that
morning. Beth felt a little queer every time she
remembered that her father was away, but she kept
busy. Now and then, as the day wore on, she tried
to decide what present she would ask her father
for.

Finally the cold day turned into a cold, blustery
winter night. David had heated the stew that their
father had left for supper. He and Beth ate every
bit of it. Now it was time to feed the cattle and
settle them down for the night, and put David's
horse and Beth's little mare into their warm box
stalls.

When Beth and David went out into the night,
the wind slammed the door shut behind them. The
sky was very black.

"It's going to snow again, I think," said David, looking up. Beth followed him to the barn, shivering. She was glad to step inside, where the warm bodies and steamy breath of their big cattle herd kept the air almost as warm as a house.

David switched on the lights. The cattle blinked in the sudden brightness. They knew what it

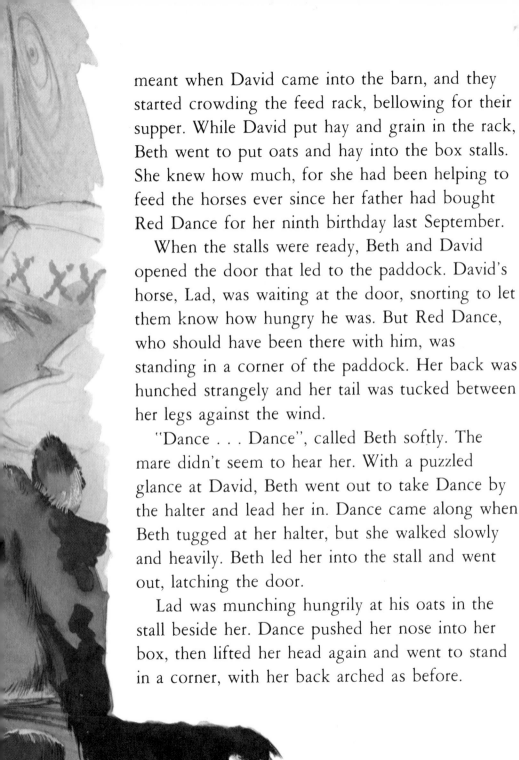

meant when David came into the barn, and they started crowding the feed rack, bellowing for their supper. While David put hay and grain in the rack, Beth went to put oats and hay into the box stalls. She knew how much, for she had been helping to feed the horses ever since her father had bought Red Dance for her ninth birthday last September.

When the stalls were ready, Beth and David opened the door that led to the paddock. David's horse, Lad, was waiting at the door, snorting to let them know how hungry he was. But Red Dance, who should have been there with him, was standing in a corner of the paddock. Her back was hunched strangely and her tail was tucked between her legs against the wind.

"Dance . . . Dance", called Beth softly. The mare didn't seem to hear her. With a puzzled glance at David, Beth went out to take Dance by the halter and lead her in. Dance came along when Beth tugged at her halter, but she walked slowly and heavily. Beth led her into the stall and went out, latching the door.

Lad was munching hungrily at his oats in the stall beside her. Dance pushed her nose into her box, then lifted her head again and went to stand in a corner, with her back arched as before.

"David, there's something wrong with
Dance," said Beth.

"What's the matter?"

"She's not eating."

David wrinkled his forehead. He hoped nothing
was going to go wrong tonight, with his father
away. He came and stood beside Beth, watching
Red Dance. Like most horses, she was usually very
greedy, especially for her oats. David had often
teased Beth that Red Dance was getting fat, but he
was worried now. He knew that when a horse
won't eat, it is probably sick.

As they watched, the little mare suddenly turned
her head around until her nose was touching her
fat side, and snapped her strong teeth. It looked as
is she was trying to bite herself.

"Oh, David. What's she doing?"

"I don't know, but she sure isn't normal. She
looks so . . . sort of uncomfortable or something."

"Let's call the vet," said Beth.

David ran out, glad to be doing something
instead of just standing there worrying. Beth's
knees felt a little weak. She sat down on a bale of hay.

"Oh, Dance," she said softly. "Don't be sick.
Please. I don't really want a present for being
good. I just want you to get better."

As she watched, Red Dance lay down in the clean yellow straw of her stall. But in a few seconds she was up again, walking up and down the stall as if something was hurting her very much.

The door opened and David came slowly into the barn.

"What did Dr. Lubinski say?" asked Beth, jumping up eagerly.

"She isn't home," replied David unhappily. "The phone rang and rang."

"Oh, no!"

David didn't know what was wrong with Red Dance, but he just couldn't go to bed and leave her. He wouldn't be able to sleep even if he tried.

"Beth, it's getting late. You go up to the house and go to bed. I'll stay here and watch Dance, and I'll try to phone Dr. Lubinski again later."

"Can't I stay here, David?"

"You should be in bed," said David, but secretly he didn't want to be alone anyway.

Beth lay down on a bed of straw bales, with loose straw as a pillow for her head. She was very comfortable. It would have been fun if she hadn't been so scared about Red Dance. David went back to the house and gathered up two old blankets, to keep them warm. While he was there he tried Dr. Lubinski's number again. But she still didn't answer.

When David came back, he found Beth asleep already. He covered her up and then sat down on a bale where he could see the mare. He pulled the blanket around his shoulders.

Red Dance was still behaving strangely. She
would stand quietly for a while, as if looking inside
herself. Then she would begin pawing and
snapping again.

As David got warmer inside the blanket, he
began to feel sleepy. The cattle had finished eating
and were lying down one by one. Their jaws as
they chewed their cuds made soothing, peaceful
sounds. David's eyes would close for a few
moments, until he blinked them open again. Finally
they closed and refused to open. He was asleep.

"David, wake up. Wake up!"

"What? What is it?" For a moment, David wondered where he was. It was early morning. Pearly grey light came through the barn windows. His back was sore and his legs were stiff from sleeping sitting up. Then he remembered Red Dance! He jumped up and ran to the stall door. Beth followed close behind him. They peered in.

"She's eating now. She looks fine!" cried Beth.

Red Dance was standing in her usual way, head down in her pile of hay. They could hear her strong teeth crunching the hay stalks.

"David, she looks . . . different somehow. Doesn't she?"

"Beth, there's something strange. What's that behind her?"

Beth opened the stall door and they both leaned down for a closer look. At the back of the stall they could see four more legs.

"It's a—"

"It's a foal, Beth! That's why she was acting so strange. She was getting ready to have a baby!"

"Oh, David. We didn't even know!"

David grinned. In his relief, he forgot how stiff and tired he felt. "Boy, I feel kind of stupid. I should have known."

David and Beth had both seen calves born on the farm, but they had never had a foal before. Now that David thought back, he realized that Red Dance had behaved just the way the cows did when they were going to have babies.

The two children tiptoed into the stall. Red Dance, her mother's instincts aroused even with these two she knew so well, whickered warningly. She backed up to face them as they came toward her foal.

"All right, girl. I know he's new," said Beth softly. "We won't touch. We'll just look."

"Isn't he beautiful? breathed David.

"Healthy, too," replied Beth happily. "You can always tell if they stand up right away like that. Like calves."

They stood for a long time, just looking at Red Dance and her bright red foal. He had a blaze of white down his face which widened out over one eye. It gave him a comical, puzzled look. He took one shaky step toward them. Then his legs folded under him and he went down in a heap beside his mother. He closed his eyes contentedly.

David suddenly came out of his trance.

"Oh, oh! It's getting late and we haven't had breakfast yet. Let's go up to the house," he said.

"Not yet. I'm not a bit hungry."

Just then they both heard the familiar sound of their father's truck crunching the gravel as it came up the driveway. Beth ran out the door into the snow.

"Daddy!"

The truck stopped in front of the barn, and their father got out quickly. Beth ran into his arms.

"How's my sweetheart? Is everything all right, son?" he added as David came out behind her.

"Just great!" said David feelingly. "How's Uncle Arthur?"

"Still very sick, but I took him to the hospital. The doctor says he'll get better there. But how are you?" asked his father, suddenly noticing the tired dark circles under David's eyes.

"Fine. We're both fine. And Dad—we have something to show you."

"What is it?"

"Come and see," Beth said, taking his sleeve and pulling him toward the barn door.

"Well, how about that?" exclaimed their father wonderingly, leaning over the stall door. "I knew that Red Dance was going to have a foal, but I didn't know it would be so soon!"

"Well, there he is," said David with a special smile over at Beth.

"He's all yours, Beth," said her father. "You'll have to think of a good name for him."

"I have a name for him already," replied Beth, who had just had a very good idea. "I'm going to call him My Present!"

If I Had A Horse

If I had a horse,
I'd like him to be
As white as the whitecaps
That ride on the sea,

Or I'd like him black
And little and trim;
Or if he were chestnut
I'd be proud of him;

I'd like him large,
A smooth dappled grey,
With heavy hoofs;
Or I'd like him bay.

You see it's like this:
I just wouldn't mind
What was his size
Or his colour or kind;

If I had a horse
I'd like him so much
I just wouldn't care
About colours and such.

Lucretia Penny

Windy's First Ride

Jo Currie

Training Windy

"Mum, can we try Windy today? Can we?" said Pam. "It's been three weeks since we brought him home. You said I could ride him soon."

"Yes, Pam. I think today's the day to begin training Windy. But before you ride him, he has to learn to walk with you on a lead," said her mother.

Windy, the small pale-gold colt with a soft white mane and tail, whinnied softly. He trotted over to where Pamela and her mother were standing. He had learned that nice things happened when they came to see him. He didn't understand people's words but he did understand the sound of their voices. In the three weeks that he had lived in the grassy paddock behind the Dennison's house, Pamela had talked softly to him whenever she brought him a treat—an apple, or a carrot, or a handful of oats.

Windy didn't know that he belonged to a girl named Pamela, nor that his own name was Windy.

In his mind he thought of Pamela as "the-little-one-who-brings-me-good-things". Mrs. Dennison was, for him, "the-big-one-who-makes-me-do-things". Mrs. Dennison wanted to train Windy to be a safe, obedient riding horse for Pamela, so Pam could ride her when she took her own horse, Sammy, for a ride.

Pamela thought about how much Windy had changed since they had got him. She remembered the day her mother brought Windy home. Mrs. Dennison had bought him from a big stable where he had lived with his mother and a herd of other horses. She brought him home, a shivering three-year-old who had never been away from the place where he was born. She turned him into the paddock with Sammy. The bumpy ride in the dark horse trailer frightened him badly and, like all horses, he was scared of anything new.

But soon, Windy decided that life here was good, and he ran around the paddock only for the joy of it. Pamela named him Windy that first day as she watched the wind move his fine, soft mane and tail while he ran.

Then there was the day Mrs. Dennison came home with a beautiful new blue halter that suited Windy's golden colouring. She brought a blue bag with a body brush and a rubber curry comb to brush mud off his body, and a soft brush to take out dust and make his coat shine.

Mrs. Dennison talked to Pamela as she groomed him. "Always let him know where you are, Pam," said her mother, "especially when you walk behind him. Horses can see anything that moves, even right behind them. Their eyes are made that way. If you move too quickly he might kick out at you because he's scared of sudden movements." So Pam always said, "Whoa, boy," softly, when she walked behind Windy, and learned to move calmly and quietly.

Now Windy was ready to learn to walk on a lead. Pamela hoped he would learn fast. She watched her mother snap a lead rope into his halter and begin to walk. at first, when Windy felt the rope pull against her halter, he pulled back, frightened. He didn't know what Mrs. Dennison wanted him to do.

"Why is he scared, Mum? You're not going to hurt him."

"No, but he doesn't know that yet, Pam. Horses hate being held at first. It makes them feel trapped."

Mrs. Dennison didn't try to drag Windy along with her. She pulled on the rope with short, gentle tugs. When Windy finally took two steps forward, she talked to him softly and scratched his back in the way he liked best. Soon Windy was walking quietly along beside Mrs. Dennison, stopping when she stopped, and turning when she turned.

"Why does the-big-one want me to walk beside her?" thought Windy to himself. "I'd rather be running free and eating grass. But when I don't go with her, something pulls at my nose and pinches. But when I do what she wants she scratches my back. So I guess I'd better do it."

When Windy was leading properly for Mrs. Dennison, she let Pam take her around. Windy behaved himself beautifully.

The Ride

A few days later Mrs. Dennison decided it was time for Windy to wear a saddle, and learn to carry Pamela on his back. While Pamela brought the saddle, saddle pad and bridle over to the fence, Mrs. Dennison snapped the lead rope into Windy's halter and made him stand still. She took the big, soft saddle pad, which would keep his back from getting sore from the leather saddle, and let him smell it. Then she laid it gently over his back, being careful not to move too quickly. Windy jumped a little when it touched his back. Mrs. Dennison picked up the pad and laid it down again many times, each time a little less gently, until he stopped being afraid of it.

"Now for the saddle," she said. She placed it quietly on his back over the pad, and drew up the girth around his stomach a little at a time. She buckled it tightly enough to keep the saddle from sliding off. Because Windy had been brushed and touched so often, the girth didn't scare him. He stood quietly.

Then Mrs. Dennison unsnapped the rope and gave Windy a gentle slap to let him know he was free. Windy walked away uncertainly. What was this thing on his back? As he walked, the stirrups of the saddle swung against his side with every step. He hated the feeling! His ears went flat with anger. He decided to get rid of whatever was on his back. He put his head down and kicked up with his hind feet. The stirrups swung harder than ever, but the saddle stayed on. He ran around the paddock, partly frightened and partly angry, bucking every few steps.

"Oooh! Mum!" cried Pam. "Will he do that with me in the saddle?"

"Not if we let him get it all over with first. He'll learn that he can't get the saddle off, and that it won't hurt him anyway."

Mrs. Dennison was right. When Windy found that the thing on his back stayed on, he stood still for a moment. The stirrups stopped swinging. Then he trotted a few steps, and the stirrups didn't scare him any more. He put his head down and started to eat grass.

"Good boy, Windy!" said Mrs. Dennison. "He learns fast, Pam. Now we'll give him one of those apples you've got in your pocket."

Pam climbed the fence and walked toward
Windy, holding the apple out. Windy trotted to
her and stopped to take the apple politely. While
Windy's strong teeth were crunching it up, Mrs.
Dennison snapped the lead rope back into his
halter and put something new on his head over the
halter. It was a leather bridle, with a hackamore
and reins. The hackamore was a strong band that
arched across the front. It touched his nose when
Mrs. Dennison pulled the reins gently. If she pulled
sharply, the hackamore would bump his nose quite
hard. Later on, Windy would learn to carry a bit in

his mouth, and to respond to signals from the reins, but for now the hackamore would make him obey.

Holding onto both the reins and the lead rope, Mrs. Dennison lifted Pam very gently into the saddle, so that her weight would come down slowly on Windy's back. She talked softly to Windy all the time, using the words he was used to. When Pam was in the saddle she slid her feet carefully into the stirrups. Pam was a little scared after seeing Windy buck, but she sat quietly in the saddle, as she did when she rode Sammy.

Mrs. Dennison took the lead rope and reins and led Windy off at a walk. With his first step he felt Pam's weight on his back and laid his ears flat again. Mrs. Dennison was watching those ears. She knew that they showed when a horse is scared or angry. She pulled sharply on the reins, bringing the hackamore down on his nose quiet hard. At the same time she said, "Whoa!" not loudly, but in a stern voice. Windy knew that voice, and he remembered the bump on his nose. He stood still, his ears up again. This time, when Mrs. Dennison led him off, he walked quietly, slowly getting used to Pam's weight on his back. Pam began to relax, too, and this helped Windy feel more sure of himself.

When they had walked around for quite a long time, Mrs. Dennison gave the reins to Pam, but kept hold of the rope.

"When we move off, squeeze his sides gently with your legs," she said, "the same as you do on Sammy . And when we stop, give a short, gentle pull on the reins. Just enough to touch his nose. It will be the signal for him to stop. Don't bump his nose. You only need to do that it he's being bad." Then she led off again, stopping and starting a lot. Soon Windy was beginning to get the idea. Squeezing with her legs meant "go". Pulling on the reins meant "stop". Pam's eyes were shining. Windy was learning so quickly!

"Can I take her around by myself, Mum?" she asked. "Without you holding the lead rope?"

Mrs. Dennison hesitated a moment. She didn't want Pam to get hurt. She looked at Windy, who was standing quietly.

"All right, Pam. Just once around, and then I think he's had enough for today."

She unsnapped the lead rope and stood back by the fence. She was ready to move quickly if Windy showed signs of getting upset. Pam squeezed very gently. Windy glanced at Mrs. Dennison and walked off on his own. Pamela used the reins to

guide him, walking close beside the fence. When they reached the place where Mrs. Dennison was standing, Windy slowed as if to stop. Pam clucked to him softly and squeezed again, and Windy moved past her.

When they reached the corner, Pam squeezed harder with one leg. She pulled on the other rein to turn him, and Windy started down the other side of the fence. When they had gone once around, Pam pulled gently on the reins and said "Whoa!" at the same time. Windy stopped, and stood still. Very quietly, without touching Windy, Pam took both feet out of the stirrups and swung a leg over, then slid to the ground.

"He did it, Mum! Isn't he good? Isn't he wonderful?"

Pam threw her arms around Windy's neck.

"He certainly is," replied her mother. "Another few lessons like that and you'll be able to come with me when I go for a ride!"

Of course, Windy didn't understand these words either. He took the apple Pam gave him and stood crunching it while they unsaddled him and took off the bridle. When they let him go, with another pat, he stood and stared at them as they walked away. He did not know that soon he would be

trotting down the roads beside Sammy, with Pam
on his back.

"So the little-one-who-brings-things wants me to
carry her on my back," thought Windy to himself
as he watched them go. "I don't see why. But there
isn't anything to be afraid of. It doesn't seem to
hurt. And the apples are delicious!"

Editors

Joe Banel
Ruta Demery
Clay Graves

Illustrations

Vlasta van Kampen: 4-5, 18-27
Joe Salina: 6-15
Wayne McKenzie: 28-29, 68-69
Lissa Calvert: 37-44
John Milne: 46-51
Eugenie Fernandes: 58-67, 80-93
Henry Fernandes: 71-79
Alan Daniel: 94-108
Huntley Brown: 111-119
Elaine Macpherson: 127-129, 147-159
Olena Kassies: 132-144
Stamps on pages 120-123 courtesy of
Mary Robson and Gustav Eikerts

Photographs

M.V. Smith, Dept. of Environmental
Biology, Univ. of Guelph: 31 (top), 33,
35 (top)
Bob Wood: 31 (bottom)
Miller Services: 35 (bottom), 50
Boris Spremo: 46-49, 51, 52
Doug Collins: 55
Birgitte Nielsen: 124
Esther Peachey: 126, 130

Acknowledgements:

"Blue Moose" by Manus Pinkwater is
reprinted from *Cricket, the Magazine for
Children*, Vol. 3, no. 5. The story was
adapted and excerpted from *Blue Moose*,
copyright© 1975 by Manus Pinkwater,
published by Dodd, Mead
and Company, Inc.

"Foal" by Mary Britton Miller is
reprinted from *Menagerie*© 1928 by
Mary Britton Miller, published by
Macmillan Company. Reprinted by
permission of James Nathan Miller.

"If I Had a Horse" by Lucretia Penny is
in the public domain. The poem was
first published in *Instructor*, December,
1935.

All other selections are used by
permission of the authors.

Typesetting: Mono Lino Typesetting
Company Ltd.
Printing and Binding: The Bryant Press
Ltd.
This book is set in 15 on 18 point
Garamond